818 Whi c.1 Whitman, Walt 10564
Walt Whitman's America

Walt Whitman's America

THE WORLD PUBLISHING COMPANY

Cleveland and New York

Walt Whitman's America

being selections from *LEAVES OF GRASS*
DEMOCRATIC VISTAS
SPECIMEN DAYS
and PORTRAITS OF LINCOLN

by James Daugherty

Published by The World Publishing Company
2231 West 110th Street, Cleveland 2, Ohio
Published simultaneously in Canada by
Nelson, Foster & Scott Ltd.
Library of Congress Catalog Card Number: 64-19998

3MP466

 Printed in the United States of America by
the Murray Printing Company, Forge Village, Massachusetts.

Dedicated to the memory of
KATHERINE S. DREIER
Founder and President of
The collection of the Societé Anonyme: Museum of Modern Art
(presented to the Yale University Art Gallery, 1950)
whose greatness of soul, generosity of mind,
and lifetime dedication to the cause of modern art
as an international manifestation of the human spirit
have so enduringly enriched the cultural and spiritual life
of America and the world.

Contents

THE AMERICAN DREAM

THE WAR 1861–1865

ABRAHAM LINCOLN

The Washington of my childhood was a sleepy southern town whose shady streets had long forgotten the tumult of the Civil War, although many of its veterans peacefully reposed in government offices. In public school I never heard the Gettysburg Address or least of all Walt Whitman's poetry.

But poetry was food and drink in the daily life of our home. THE LIBRARY OF POETRY AND SONG *was a worn volume from which my father read aloud with such contagious delight that we looked forward to the long winter evenings filled with the sound and splendor of great poetry. This and a half-dozen enormous volumes all illustrated by Doré provided a romantic background that promised a very museful career.*

There was none of Whitman's poetry in the LIBRARY OF POETRY AND SONG *and I suppose my father disapproved of him for the same reason that Emily Dickinson wrote, "I have not read Mr. Whitman but have been told he is disgraceful." My first encounter with Whitman was to be outside the United States.*

Generously my parents consented to my attending the art school of the Pennsylvania Academy of Fine Arts. Philadelphia was a fascinating city to a youngster in his first winter away from home and I soon found myself at ease in the big shabby studios of the old school on Broad St. Once a week the famous portrait painter William M. Chase came down from New York to instruct his classes. He was an awesome figure in high silk hat and frock coat, striped pants, white vest, spats, and gold-headed cane. He wore a monocle on a wide black ribbon and his bushy eyebrows and prodigious upturned mustaches gave his handsome face a romantic ferocity.

The monitor of the class, who had placed a blank convas and easel beside the model, handed the master a large palette charged with color and a fistful of clean brushes. Seizing them he poised for a few moments before making a series of rushes upon the canvas, retiring from each attack with dramatic posturing. During the whole process he emitted through his mustaches a hissing sound that somehow gave a mysterious solemnity and importance to the scene. In less than an hour, with marvelous deftness, he had brushed in a completely realized portrait. It was so dazzling a performance that we were left breathless and subdued. Afterward he told anecdotes of his association with James McNeill Whistler and John Singer Sargent. Sargent had painted Chase's portrait in full regalia and Chase himself had painted a full-length portrait of Whistler, who had called it a "monstrous lampoon" much to Chase's amusement.

While I was in Philadelphia, my father was appointed European representative of the U. S. Department of Agriculture with headquarters in London. I finished the school year at the Academy and embarked with my boon companion the sculptor Hunt Diederick on the old freighter WESTERNLAND. *The trip took twelve days and the fare was forty dollars.*

London was pure enchantment. The continuous rumble of hansom cabs and horse-drawn buses on wooden pavements, the streets haunted with history, and the white fog that wrapped the city in silver mystery all cast their spell of wonder and delight. I haunted the galleries, museums, abbeys and lingered along the Thames embankment where Whistler, Turner, Carlyle, Wilde, and the great Victorians had so recently walked.

One soon learned the cockney lingo and chivvied with costers, navvies, and flower girls during bank holidays on the green at Wormwood Scrubs and in pushcart markets on Portobello Road on teeming Saturday nights. This was the great age of the Music Hall artists and the symphonies at Albert Hall. Ah! to be footloose and free and sixteen in that lost world of Europe which was so soon to be shattered by the terrible salvos of the First World War.

I attended the London School of Art which occupied studios in a courtyard behind a stone wall with a green door on Stratford Road, South Kensington. A group of English students and several Americans made up the classes and once a week Frank Brangwyn came from his Hammersmith studio and painted sumptuous color patterns over our feeble daubs. He was at forty the most virile painter in England and had just completed the great mural panels for the Skinners' Guild Hall. Brangwyn had worked for William Morris and was now painting huge canvases that were really opulent tapestries so gorgeous that at the annual Royal Academy Exhibition they made everything else in the show look empty and tired.

One day there appeared at the school a young Californian with a copy of LEAVES OF GRASS *in his pocket. I had never read a line of it. Was this really my America, this splendor of democracy, this new world of affirmation and fraternity and hope? We read and chanted and roared our favorite passages to our bewildered British comrades.*

LEAVES OF GRASS *got under my skin and into my bones. For the first time I felt the meaning and power of that majestic word "America," and through Whitman's eyes I dimly glimpsed the grandeur of its possibilities. I must return to my country at once and forever.*

Farewell Europe, the museums, good-bye King Arthur! Good-bye dear London friends and all you genial hospitable Londoners. I shall always love you!

As the tugs nosed the great liner up the harbor we caught sight of the towers of Manhattan hung in the morning haze. They seemed to drift toward us growing higher and higher. We passed under the great green Lady with the Lamp, silent, subdued by thoughts and feelings beyond words. Suddenly we were ashore on American soil, each on his own, an individual American person, a drop in the vast rushing torrents of American life—of Walt Whitman's America, our America.

Some notes on Whitman for today:

These brief selections from Walt Whitman's major works are only samples to invite and tempt you to the great adventure of reading all his poems and prose.

You will of course choose and reject, agree and disagree with his tumultuous philosophies, but as you read and reread them your thoughts about America will surely expand, for they do what Emily Dickinson calls "joggle the mind" and expand the spirit toward wider horizons along new and unexplored paths; and I think this is good in a world rushing so swiftly toward unlimited possibilities.

Too few Americans have read Whitman's great prose poem DEMOCRATIC VISTAS. *Few thinkers have ever speculated so deeply on the past, present, and future of democracy, and its meaning for the world and humanity. Today more than ever it is good to pause in our fabulous age of space and power to ask ourselves, "Who and what are we and where are we going so fast?"*

One hundred years after the Civil War, much is still being written about that great struggle, but nothing brings so grimly alive its heroism and agony as Whitman's firsthand account of the hospitals in wartime Washington and the aftermath of battles, seen through the eyes of a great poet and a great soul. We feel the grandeur of Lincoln as Whitman felt it, peering into his sad mysterious face as they passed so often on the streets of Washington. We too have felt the terrible shock of a beloved President assassinated. It is as if Whitman had written for us today his great funeral dirge "When Lilacs Last in the Door-yard Bloom'd." "The most sonorous anthem ever chanted in the church of the world" Swinburne once called it.

More than ever Whitman's message is for all of us today and tomorrow, for he sings of courage and joy, of hope and faith in the American destiny. He declares and celebrates in splendid affirmation our dearest hope and faith that the Founders of our nation have builded on enduring truth and have not built in vain.

I Hear America Singing

I Hear America Singing

I HEAR AMERICA SINGING, the varied carols I hear;
Those of mechanics—each one singing his, as it should be, blithe and strong;
The carpenter singing his, as he measures his plank or beam,
The mason singing his, as he makes ready for work, or leaves off work;
The boatman singing what belongs to him in his boat—the deck-hand singing on the steamboat deck;
The shoemaker singing as he sits on his bench—the hatter singing as he stands;
The wood-cutter's song—the ploughboy's, on his way in the morning, or at the noon intermission, or at sundown;
The delicious singing of the mother—or of the young wife at work—or of the girl sewing or washing—Each singing what belongs to her, and to none else;
The day what belongs to the day—At night, the party of young fellows, robust, friendly,
Singing, with open mouths, their strong melodious songs.

Song of Myself

I CELEBRATE MYSELF;
And what I assume you shall assume;
For every atom belonging to me, as good belongs to you.

I loafe and invite my Soul;
I lean and loafe at my ease, observing a spear of summer grass.

Houses and rooms are full of perfumes—the shelves are crowded
with perfumes;
I breathe the fragrance myself, and know it and like it;
The distillation would intoxicate me also, but I shall not let it.

The atmosphere is not a perfume—it has no taste of the distillation—it is odorless;
It is for my mouth forever—I am in love with it;
I will go to the bank by the wood, and become undisguised and naked;
I am mad for it to be in contact with me.

* * *

The spotted hawk swoops by and accuses me—he complains of my gab and my loitering.

I too am not a bit tamed—I too am untranslatable;
I sound my barbaric yawp over the roofs of the world.

The last scud of day holds back for me;
It flings my likeness after the rest, and true as any, on the shadow'd
wilds;
It coaxes me to the vapor and the dusk.

I depart as air—I shake my white locks at the runaway sun;
I effuse my flesh in eddies, and drift it in lacy jags.
I bequeathe myself to the dirt, to grow from the grass I love;
If you want me again, look for me under your bootsoles.

You will hardly know who I am, or what I mean;
But I shall be good health to you nevertheless,
And filter and fibre your blood.

Failing to fetch me at first, keep encouraged;
Missing me one place, search another;
I stop somewhere, waiting for you.

Song of the Open Road

AFOOT AND LIGHT-HEARTED, I take to the open road,
Healthy, free, the world before me,
The long brown path before me, leading wherever I choose.

Henceforth I ask not good fortune—I myself am good fortune;
Henceforth I whimper no more, postpone no more, need nothing,
Strong and content, I travel the open road.

The earth—that is sufficient;
I do not want the constellations any nearer;
I know they are very well where they are;
I know they suffice for those who belong to them.

(Still here I carry my old delicious burdens;
I carry them, men and women—I carry them with me wherever
I go;
I swear it is impossible for me to get rid of them;
I am fill'd with them, and I will fill them in return.)

* * *

From this hour, freedom!
From this hour I ordain myself loos'd of limits and imaginary
lines,
Going where I list, my own master, total and absolute,
Listening to others, and considering well what they say,
Pausing, searching, receiving, contemplating,
Gently, but with undeniable will, divesting myself of the holds
that would hold me.

I inhale great draughts of space;
The east and the west are mine, and the north and the south are
mine.

I am larger, better than I thought;
I did not know I held so much goodness.
All seems beautiful to me;
I can repeat over to men and women, You have done such good
to me, I would do the same to you. . . .

Years of the Modern

YEARS OF THE MODERN! years of the unperform'd!
Your horizon rises—I see it parting away for more august dramas;
I see not America only—I see not only Liberty's nation, but other nations preparing;
I see tremendous entrances and exits—I see new combinations—I see the solidarity of races;
I see that force advancing with irresistible power on the world's stage;
(Have the old forces, the old wars, played their parts? are the acts suitable to them closed?)

I see Freedom, completely arm'd, and victorious, and very haughty, with Law on one side, and Peace on the other,
A stupendous Trio, all issuing forth against the idea of caste;
—What historic denouements are these we so rapidly approach? . . .
—What whispers are these, O lands, running ahead of you, passing under the seas?
Are all nations communing? is there going to be but one heart to the globe?
Is humanity forming, en-masse?—for lo! tyrants tremble, crowns grow dim;
The earth, restive, confronts a new era, perhaps a general divine war;
No one knows what will happen next—such portents fill the days and nights;
Years prophetical! the space ahead as I walk, as I vainly try to pierce it, is full of phantoms;
Unborn deeds, things soon to be, project their shapes around me;
This incredible rush and heat—this strange extatic fever of dreams, O years! . . .

Song of the Broad-axe

WEAPON, shapely, naked, wan!
Head from the mother's bowels drawn!
Wooded flesh and metal bone! limb only one, and lip only one!
Gray-blue leaf by red-heat grown! helve produced from a little seed sown!
Resting the grass amid and upon,
To be lean'd, and to lean on.

Strong shapes, and attributes of strong shapes—masculine trades, sights and sounds.

* * *

The beauty of all adventurous and daring persons,

The beauty of wood-boys and wood-men, with their clear untrimm'd faces,
The beauty of independence, departure, actions that rely on themselves,
The American contempt for statutes and ceremonies, the boundless impatience of restraint,
The loose drift of character, the inkling through random types, the solidification;
The butcher in the slaughter-house, the hands aboard schooners and sloops, the raftsman, the pioneer,
Lumbermen in their winter camp, day-break in the woods, stripes of snow on the limbs of trees, the occasional snapping,
The glad clear sound of one's own voice, the merry song, the natural life of the woods, the strong day's work,
The blazing fire at night, the sweet taste of supper, the talk, the bed of hemlock boughs, and the bear-skin. . . .

Crossing Brooklyn Ferry

FLOOD-TIDE BELOW ME! I watch you face to face;
Clouds of the west! sun there half an hour high! I see you also
    face to face.

Crowds of men and women attired in the usual costumes! how
    curious you are to me!
On the ferry-boats, the hundreds and hundreds that cross, return-
    ing home, are more curious to me than you suppose;
And you that shall cross from shore to shore years hence, are
    more to me, and more in my meditations, than you might
    suppose.

* * *

Others will enter the gates of the ferry, and cross from shore to
shore;
Others will watch the run of the flood-tide;
Others will see the shipping of Manhattan north and west, and
the heights of Brooklyn to the south and east;
Others will see the islands large and small;
Fifty years hence, others will see them as they cross, the sun half
an hour high;
A hundred years hence, or ever so many hundred years hence,
others will see them,
Will enjoy the sunset, the pouring in of the flood-tide, the falling
back to the sea of the ebb-tide.

It avails not, neither time or place—distance avails not. . . .

Cavalry Crossing a Ford

A LINE IN LONG ARRAY, where they wind betwixt green islands;
They take a serpentine course—their arms flash in the sun—
Hark to the musical clank;
Behold the silvery river—in it the splashing horses, loitering, stop to drink;
Behold the brown-faced men—each group, each person, a picture —the negligent rest on the saddles;
Some emerge on the opposite bank—others are just entering the ford—while,
Scarlet, and blue, and snowy white,
The guidon flags flutter gaily in the wind.

When Lilacs Last in the Door-yard Bloom'd

WHEN LILACS LAST in the door-yard bloom'd,
And the great star early droop'd in the western sky in the night,
I mourn'd—and yet shall mourn with ever-returning spring.

O ever-returning spring! trinity sure to me you bring;
Lilac blooming perennial, and drooping star in the west,
And thought of him I love.

O powerful, western, fallen star!
O shades of night! O moody, tearful night!
O great star disappear'd! O the black murk that hides the star!
O cruel hands that hold me powerless! O helpless soul of me!
O harsh surrounding cloud, that will not free my soul!

In the door-yard fronting an old farm-house, near the white-
wash'd palings,
Stands the lilac bush, tall-growing, with heart-shaped leaves of
rich green,
With many a pointed blossom, rising, delicate, with the perfume
strong I love,
With every leaf a miracle . . . and from this bush in the door-yard,
With delicate-color'd blossoms, and heart-shaped leaves of rich
green,
A sprig, with its flower, I break.

In the swamp, in secluded recesses,
A shy and hidden bird is warbling a song.
Solitary, the thrush,
The hermit, withdrawn to himself, avoiding the settlements,
Sings by himself a song.
Song of the bleeding throat!
Death's outlet song of life—(for well, dear brother, I know
If thou wast not gifted to sing, thou would'st surely die.)

Over the breast of the spring, the land, amid cities,
Amid lanes, and through old woods, (where lately the violets
peep'd from the ground, spotting the gray debris;)
Amid the grass in the fields each side of the lanes—passing the
endless grass;
Passing the yellow-spear'd wheat, every grain from its shroud in
the dark-brown fields uprising;
Passing the apple-tree blows of white and pink in the orchards;
Carrying a corpse to where it shall rest in the grave,
Night and day journeys a coffin. . . .

Underneath All, Individuals

Underneath all, individuals!
I swear nothing is good to me now that ignores individuals,
The American compact is altogether with individuals,
The only government is that which makes minute of individuals,
The only theory of the universe is directed to one single individual
—namely, to You. . . .

O I see now, flashing, that this America is only you and me,
Its power, weapons, testimony, are you and me,
Its crimes, lies, thefts, defections, slavery, are you and me,
Its Congress is you and me—the officers, capitols, armies, ships,
are you and me,
Its endless gestations of new States are you and me,
The war—that war so bloody and grim—the war I will hence-
forth forget—was you and me,
Natural and artificial are you and me,
Freedom, language, poems, employments, are you and me,
Past, present, future, are you and me. . . .

Pioneers! O Pioneers!

Come, my tan-faced children,
Follow well in order, get your weapons ready;
Have you your pistols? have you your sharp edged axes?
Pioneers! O pioneers!

For we cannot tarry here,
We must march my darlings, we must bear the brunt of danger,
We, the youthful sinewy races, all the rest on us depend,
Pioneers! O pioneers!

O you youths, western youths,
So impatient, full of action, full of manly pride and friendship,
Plain I see you, western youths, see you tramping with the foremost,
Pioneers! O pioneers!

Have the elder races halted?
Do they droop and end their lesson, wearied, over there beyond the seas?
We take up the task eternal, and the burden, and the lesson,
Pioneers! O pioneers!

All the past we leave behind;
We debouch upon a newer, mightier world, varied world,
Fresh and strong the world we seize, world of labor and the march,
Pioneers! O pioneers!

* * *

Has the night descended?
Was the road of late so toilsome? did we stop discouraged, nodding on our way?
Yet a passing hour I yield you, in your tracks to pause oblivious,
Pioneers! O pioneers!

Till with sound of trumpet,
Far, far off the day-break call—hark! how loud and clear I hear it wind;
Swift! to the head of the army!—swift! spring to your places,
Pioneers! O pioneers!

The American Dream

Into a Brotherhood, a Family

DEMOCRACY . . . ALONE CAN BIND, and ever seeks to bind, all nations, all men, of however various and distant lands, into a brotherhood, a family. It is the old, yet ever-modern dream of earth, out of her eldest and her youngest, her fond philosophers and poets. Not that half [of democracy] only, individualism, which isolates. There is another half, which is adhesiveness or love, that fuses, ties, and aggregates, making the races comrades, and fraternizing all.

Both are to be vitalized by religion (sole worthiest elevator of man or State) breathing into the proud, material tissues, the breath of life. For I say at the core of democracy, finally, is the religious element. All the religions, old and new, are there. Nor may the scheme step forth, clothed in resplendent beauty and command, till these, bearing the best, the latest fruit, the spiritual, shall fully appear.

The Idea of the Women of America

DEMOCRACY, in silence, biding its time, ponders its own ideals, not of literature and art only—not of men only, but of women. The idea of the women of America (extricated from this daze, this fossil and unhealthy air which hangs about the word *lady*) developed, raised to become the robust equals, workers, and, it may be, even practical and political deciders with the men—greater than man, we may admit, through their divine maternity, always their towering, emblematical attribute—but great, at any rate, as man, in all departments; or, rather, capable of being so, soon as they realize it, and can bring themselves to give up toys and fictions, and launch forth, as men do, amid real, independent, stormy life.

The Prophetic Vision

THOUGH NOT FOR US the joy of entering at the last the conquered city—not ours the chance ever to see with our own eyes the peerless power and splendid *éclat* of the democratic principle, arrived at meridian, filling the world with effulgence and majesty far beyond those of past history's kings, or all dynastic sway—there is yet, to whoever is eligible among us, the prophetic vision, the joy of being tossed in the brave turmoil of these times—the promulgation and the path, obedient, lowly reverent to the voice, the gesture of the god, or holy ghost, which others see not, hear not—with the proud consciousness that amid whatever clouds, seductions, or heart-wearying postponements, we have never deserted, never despaired, never abandoned the faith.

Mannahatta

I WAS ASKING for something specific and perfect for my city,
Whereupon, lo! upsprang the aboriginal name!

Now I see what there is in a name, a word, liquid, sane, unruly,
musical, self-sufficient;
I see that the word of my city is that word up there,
Because I see that word nested in nests of water-bays, superb,
with tall and wonderful spires,
Rich, hemm'd thick all around with sailships and steamships—
an island sixteen miles long, solid-founded,

Numberless crowded streets—high growths of iron, slender, strong, light, splendidly uprising toward clear skies;
Tide swift and ample, well-loved by me, toward sun-down,
The flowing sea-currents, the little islands, larger adjoining islands, the heights, the villas,
The countless masts, the white shore-steamers, the lighters, the ferry-boats, the black sea-steamers well-model'd;
The down-town streets, the jobbers' houses of business—the houses of business of the ship-merchants, and money-brokers—the river-streets;
Immigrants arriving, fifteen or twenty thousand in a week;
The carts hauling goods—the manly race of drivers of horses—the brown-faced sailors;
The summer air, the bright sun shining, and the sailing clouds aloft;
The winter snows, the sleigh-bells—the broken ice in the river, passing along, up or down, with the flood-tide or ebb-tide;
The mechanics of the city, the masters, well-form'd, beautiful-faced, looking you straight in the eyes;
Trottoirs throng'd—vehicles—Broadway—the women—the shops and shows,
The parades, processions, bugles playing, flags flying, drums beating;
A million people—manners free and superb—open voices—hospitality—the most courageous and friendly young men;
The free city! no slaves! no owners of slaves!
The beautiful city, the city of hurried and sparkling waters! the city of spires and masts!
The city nested in bays! my city! . . .

A Single New Thought

TO THE OSTENT of the senses and eyes, I know, the influences which stamp the world's history are wars, uprisings or downfalls of dynasties, changeful movement of trade, important inventions, navigation, military or civil governments, advent of powerful personalities, conquerors, etc. These of course play their part; yet, it may be, a single new thought, imagination, abstract principle, even literary style, fit for the time, put in shape by some great literatus, and projected among mankind, may duly cause changes, growths, removals, greater than the longest and bloodiest war, or the most stupendous merely political, dynastic, or commercial overturn.

Ye Powerful and Resplendent Ones!

For us, along the great highways of time, those monuments stand—those forms of majesty and beauty. For us those beacons burn through all the nights. Unknown Egyptians, graving hieroglyphs; Hindus, with hymn and apothegm and endless epic; Hebrew prophet, with spirituality, as in flashes of lightning, conscience like red-hot iron; plaintive songs and screams of vengeance for tyrannies and enslavement; Christ, with bent head, brooding love and peace, like a dove; Greek, creating eternal shapes of physical and aesthetic proportion!

Roman, lord of satire, the sword, and the codex;—of the figures, some far off and veiled, others nearer and visible; Dante, stalking with lean form, nothing but fiber, not a grain of superfluous flesh; Angelo, and the great painters, architects, musicians; rich Shakespeare, luxuriant as the sun, artist and singer of feudalism in its sunset, with all the gorgeous colors, owner thereof, and using them at will; and so to such as German Kant and Hegel, where they, though near us, leaping over the ages, sit again, impassive, imperturbable, like the Egyptian gods. Of these, and the like of these, is it too much, indeed, to return to our favorite figure, and view them as orbs and systems of orbs, moving in free paths in the spaces of that other heaven, the cosmic intellect, the soul?

Ye powerful and resplendent ones! ye were, in your atmospheres, grown not for America, but rather for her foes, the feudal and the old—while our genius is democratic and modern.

A Resplendent Person

My dear mother once described to me a resplendent person, down on Long Island, whom she knew in early days. She was known by the name of the Peacemaker. She was well toward eighty years old, of happy and sunny temperament, had always lived on a farm, and was very neighborly, sensible, and discreet, an invariable and welcomed favorite, especially with young married women. She had numerous children and grandchildren. She was uneducated, but possessed a native dignity. She had come to be a tacitly agreed upon domestic regulator, judge, settler of difficulties, shepherdess, the reconciler in the land. She was a sight to draw near and look upon, with her large figure, her profuse snow-white hair (uncoifed by any headdress or cap), dark eyes, clear complexion, sweet breath, and peculiar personal magnetism.

The foregoing portraits, I admit, are frightfully out of line from these imported models of womanly personality—the stock feminine characters of the current novelists, or of the foreign court poems (Ophelias, Enids, princesses, or ladies of one thing or another), which fill the envying dreams of so many poor girls, and are accepted by our men, too, as supreme ideals of feminine excellence to be sought after. But I present mine just for a change.

Then there are mutterings (we will not now stop to heed them here, but they must be heeded), of something more revolutionary. The day is coming when the deep questions of woman's entrance amid the arenas of practical life, politics, the suffrage, etc., will not only be argued all around us, but may be put to decision, and real experiment.

America Is Doing Very Well

IT IS THE FASHION among dilettanti and fops (perhaps I myself am not guiltless), to decry the whole formulation of the active politics of America, as beyond redemption, and to be carefully kept away from. See you that you do not fall into this error. America, it may be, is doing very well upon the whole, notwithstanding these antics of the parties and their leaders, these half-brained nominees, and many ignorant ballots, and many elected failures and blatherers. It is the dilettanti, and all who shirk their duty, who are not doing well. As for you, I advise you to enter more strongly yet into politics. I advise every young man to do so. Always inform yourself; always do the best you can; always vote.

The People

THE PEOPLE! Like our huge earth itself, which, to ordinary scansion, is full of vulgar contradictions and offense, man, viewed in the lump, displeases, and is a constant puzzle and affront to the merely educated classes. The rare, cosmical, artist-mind, lit with the Infinite, alone confronts his manifold and oceanic qualities—but taste, intelligence, and culture (so-called), have been against the masses, and remain so. . . . But I know nothing more rare, even in this country, than a fit scientific estimate and reverent appreciation of the People—of their measureless wealth of latent power and capacity, their vast, artistic contrasts of lights and shades—with, in America, their entire reliability in emergencies, and a certain breadth of historic grandeur, of peace or war, far surpassing all the vaunted samples of book-heroes, or any *haut ton* coteries, in all the records of the world.

The Average Man

I HAIL WITH JOY the oceanic, variegated, intense practical energy, the demand for facts, even the business materialism of the current age, our States. But woe to the age and land in which these things, movements, stopping at themselves, do not tend to ideas. As fuel to flame, and flame to the heavens, so must wealth, science, materialism—even this democracy of which we make so much—unerringly feed the highest mind, the soul. Infinitude the flight: fathomless the mystery. Man, so diminutive, dilates beyond the sensible universe, competes with, outcopes space and time, meditating even one great idea. Thus, and thus only, does a human being, his spirit, ascend above, and justify objective Nature, which, probably nothing in itself, is incredibly and divinely serviceable, indispensable, real, here.

Did You, Too, O Friend, Suppose

DID YOU, TOO, O friend, suppose democracy was only for elections, for politics, and for a party name? I say democracy is only of use there that it may pass on and come to its flower and fruits in manners, in the highest forms of interaction between men, and their beliefs—in religion, literature, colleges, and schools—democracy in all public and private life, and in the army and navy. I have intimated that, as a paramount scheme, it has yet few or no full realizers and believers. I do not see, either, that it owes any serious thanks to noted propagandists or champions, or has been essentially helped, though often harmed, by them. It has been and is carried on by all the moral forces, and by trade, finance, machinery, intercommunications, and, in fact, by all the developments of history, and can no more be stopped than the tides, or the earth in its orbit.

Vive, the Attack

POLITICAL DEMOCRACY, as it exists and practically works in America, with all its threatening evils, supplies a training school for making first-class men. It is life's gymnasium, not of good only, but of all. We try often, though we fall back often. A brave delight, fit for freedom's athletes, fills these arenas, and fully satisfies, out of the action in them, irrespective of success. Whatever we do not attain, we at any rate attain the experiences of the fight, the hardening of the strong campaign, and throb with currents of attempt at least. Time is ample. Let the victors come after us.

Not for nothing does evil play its part among us. Judging from the main portions of the history of the world, so far, justice is always in jeopardy, peace walks amid hourly pitfalls, and of slavery, misery, meanness, the craft of tyrants, and the credulity of the populace, in some of the protean forms, no voice can at any time say, They are not. The clouds break a little, and the sun shines out—but soon and certain the lowering darkness falls again, as if to last forever.

Yet is there an immortal courage and prophecy in every sane soul that cannot, must not, under any circumstances, capitulate. *Vive,* the attack—the perennial assault! *Vive,* the unpopular cause—the spirit that audaciously aims—the never-abandoned efforts, pursued the same amid opposing proofs and precedents.

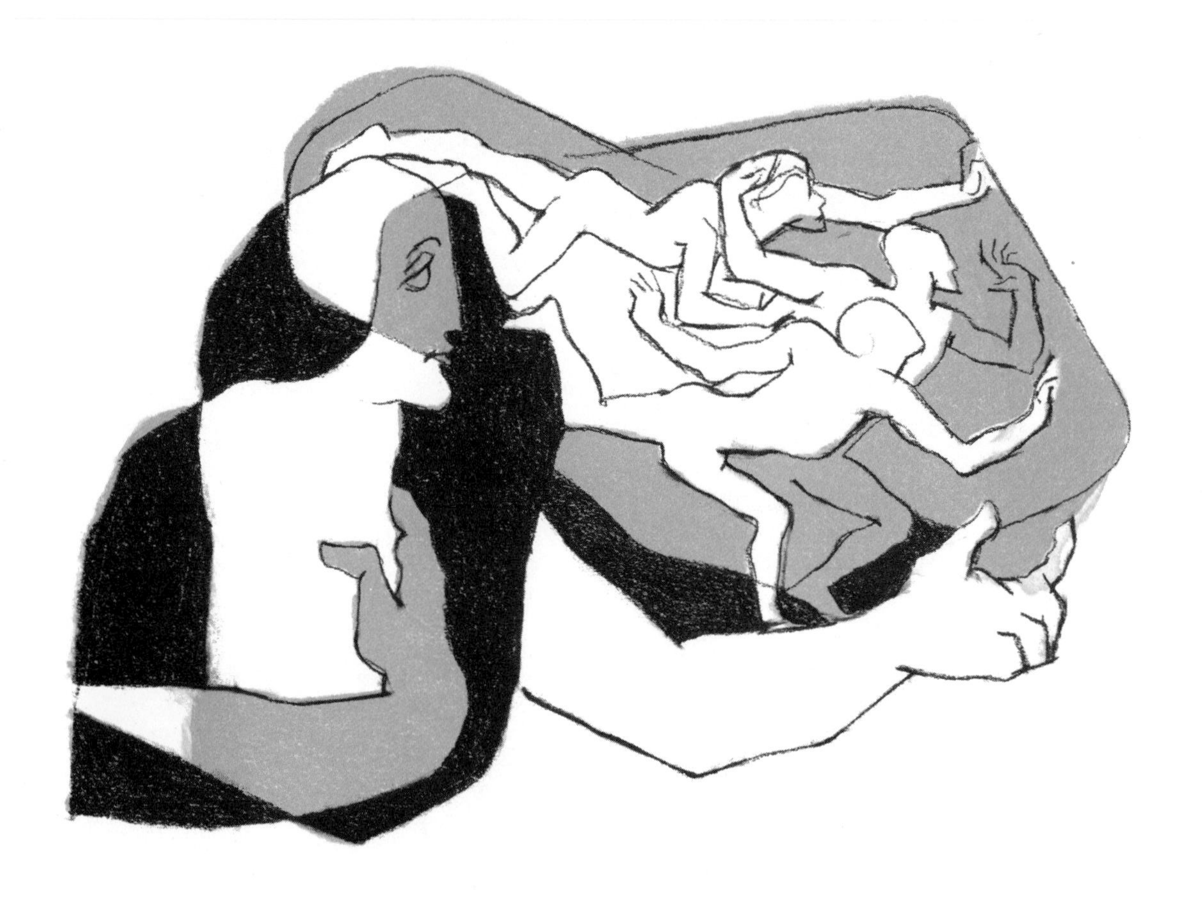

The Best Culture

THE BEST CULTURE will always be that of the manly and courageous instincts, and loving perceptions, and of self-respect—aiming to form, over this continent, an idiocrasy of universalism, which, true child of America, will bring joy to its mother, returning to her in her own spirit, recruiting myriads of offspring, able, natural, perceptive, tolerant, devout believers in her, America, and with some definite instinct why and for what she has arisen, most vast, most formidable of historic births, and is, now and here, with wonderful step, journeying through Time.

The War
1861–1865

Sinewy With Unconquerable Resolution

PROBABLY no future age can know, but I well know, how the gist of this fiercest and most resolute of the world's warlike contentions resided exclusively in the unnamed, unknown rank and file; and how the brunt of its labor of death was, to all essential purposes, volunteered. The People, of their own choice, fighting, dying for their own idea, insolently attacked by the secession-slave-power, and its very existence imperiled. Descending to detail, entering any of the armies, and mixing with the private soldiers, we see and have seen august spectacles.

We have seen the alacrity with which the American-born populace, the peaceablest and most good-natured race in the world, and the most personally independent and intelligent, and the least fitted to submit to the irksomeness and exasperation of regimental discipline, sprang, at the first tap of the drum, to arms—not for gain, nor even glory, nor to repel invasion—but for an emblem, a mere abstraction—for the life, *the safety of the flag*.

We have seen the unequaled docility and obedience of these soldiers. We have seen them tried long and long by hopelessness, mismanagement, and by defeat; have seen the incredible slaughter toward or through which the armies (as at first Fredericksburg, and afterward at the Wilderness), still unhesitatingly obey'd orders to advance. We have seen them in trench, or crouching behind breastwork, or tramping in deep mud, or amid pouring rain or thick-falling snow, or under forced marches in hottest summer (as on the road to get to Gettysburg)—vast suffocating swarms, divisions, corps, with every single man so grimed and black with sweat and dust, his own mother would not have known him—his clothes all dirty, stained and torn, with sour, accumulated sweat for perfume—many a comrade, perhaps a brother, sun-struck, staggering out, dying, by the roadside, of exhaustion —yet the great bulk bearing steadily on, cheery enough, hollow-bellied from hunger, but sinewy with unconquerable resolution.

The Battle of Bull Run, July 1861

ALL THIS SORT OF FEELING was destin'd to be arrested and revers'd by a terrible shock—the battle of first Bull Run—certainly, as we now know it, one of the most singular fights on record. (All battles, and their results, are far more matters of accident than is generally thought; but this was throughout a casualty, a chance. Each side supposed it had won, till the last moment. One had, in point of fact, just the same right to be routed as the other. By a fiction, or series of fictions, the national forces at the last moment exploded in a panic and fled from the field.)

The defeated troops commenced pouring into Washington over the Long Bridge at daylight on Monday, 22nd—day drizzling all through with rain. The Saturday and Sunday of the battle (20th, 21st), had been parch'd and hot to an extreme—the dust, the grime and smoke, in layers, sweated in, follow'd by other layers again sweated in, absorbed by those excited souls—their clothes all saturated with the clay-powder filling the air—stirr'd up everywhere on the dry roads and trodden fields by the regiments, swarming wagons, artillery, etc.—all the men with this coating of murk and sweat and rain, now recoiling back, pouring over the Long Bridge—a horrible march of twenty miles, returning to Washington baffled, humiliated, panic-struck. Where are the vaunts, and the proud boasts with which you went forth? Where are your banners, and your bands of music, and your ropes to bring back your prisoners? Well, there isn't a band playing—and there isn't a flag but clings ashamed and lank to its staff.

The sun rises, but shines not. The men appear, at first sparsely and shamefaced enough, then thicker, in the streets of Washington—appear in Pennsylvania Avenue, and on the steps and basement entrances. They come along in disorderly mobs, some in squads, stragglers, companies. Occasionally, a rare regiment, in perfect order, with its officers (some gaps, dead, the true braves), marching in silence, with lowering faces, stern, weary to sinking, all black and dirty, but every man with his musket, and stepping alive; but these are the exceptions.

Sidewalks of Pennsylvania Avenue, Fourteenth Street, etc., crowded, jamm'd with citizens, darkies, clerks, everybody, lookers-on; women in the windows, curious expressions from faces, as those swarms of dirt-covered return'd soldiers there (will they never end?) move by; but nothing said, no comments; (half our lookers-on secesh of the most venomous kind—they say nothing; but the devil snickers in their faces). During the forenoon Washington gets all over motley with these defeated soldiers—queer-looking objects, strange eyes and faces, drench'd (the steady rain drizzles on all day) and fearfully worn, hungry, haggard, blister'd in the feet.

Good people (but not over-many of them either), hurry up

something for their grub. They put wash kettles on the fire, for soup, for coffee. They set tables on the sidewalks—wagonloads of bread are purchas'd, swiftly cut in stout chunks. Here are two aged ladies, beautiful, the first in the city for culture and charm, they stand with store of eating and drink at an improvis'd table of rough plank, and give food, and have the store replenish'd from their house every half-hour all that day; and there in the rain they stand, active, silent, white-hair'd, and give food, though the tears stream down their cheeks, almost without intermission, the whole time.

Amid the deep excitement, crowds and motion, and desperate eagerness, it seems strange to see many, very many, of the soldiers sleeping—in the midst of all, sleeping sound. They drop down anywhere, on the steps of houses, up close by the basements or fences, on the sidewalk, aside on some vacant lot, and deeply sleep. A poor seventeen- or eighteen-year-old boy lies there, on the stoop of a grand house; he sleeps so calmly, so profoundly. Some clutch their muskets firmly even in sleep. Some in squads; comrades, brothers, close together—and on them, as they lie, sulkily drips the rain.

As afternoon pass'd, and evening came, the streets, the barrooms, knots everywhere, listeners, questioners, terrible yarns, bugaboo, mask'd batteries, our regiment all cut up, etc.—stories and story tellers, windy, bragging, vain centers of street crowds. Resolution, manliness, seem to have abandon'd Washington. The principal hotel, Willard's, is full of shoulder straps—thick, crush'd, creeping with shoulder straps. (I see them, and must have a word with them. There you are, shoulder straps!—but where are your companies? where are your men? Incompetents! never tell me of chances of battle, of getting stray'd, and the like. I think this is your work, this retreat, after all. Sneak, blow, put on airs there in Willard's sumptuous parlors and barrooms, or anywhere—no explanation shall save you. Bull Run is your work; had you been half or one-tenth worthy your men, this would never have happen'd.)

Meantime, in Washington, among the great persons and their entourage, a mixture of awful consternation, uncertainty, rage, shame, helplessness, and stupefying disappointment. The worst is not only imminent, but already here. In a few hours—perhaps before the next meal—the secesh generals, with their victorious hordes, will be upon us. The dream of humanity, the vaunted Union we thought so strong, so impregnable—lo! it seems already smash'd like a china plate. One bitter, bitter hour—perhaps proud America will never again know such an hour. She must pack and fly—no time to spare. Those white palaces—the dome-crown'd Capitol there on the hill, so stately over the trees—shall they be left—or destroy'd first? For it is certain that the talk among certain of the magnates and officers and clerks and officials everywhere, for twenty-four hours in and around Washington after Bull Run, was loud and undisguised for yielding out and out, and substituting the southern rule, and Lincoln promptly abdicating and departing. If the secesh officers and forces had immediately follow'd, and by a bold Napoleonic movement had enter'd Washington the first day, (or even the second), they could have had things their own way, and a powerful faction north to back them.

One of our returning colonels express'd in public that night, amid a swarm of officers and gentlemen in a crowded room, the opinion that it was useless to fight, that the Southerners had made their title clear, and that the best course for the national government to pursue was to desist from any further attempt at stopping them, and admit them again to the lead, on the best terms they were willing to grant. Not a voice was rais'd against this judgment amid that large crowd of officers and gentlemen. (The fact is, the hour was one of the three or four of those crises we had then and afterward, during the fluctuations of four years, when human eyes appear'd at least just as likely to see the last breath of the Union as to see it continue.)

Cash Is Not Amiss

As a very large proportion of the wounded came up from the front without a cent of money in their pockets, I soon discover'd that it was about the best thing I could do to raise their spirits, and show them that somebody cared for them, and practically felt a fatherly or brotherly interest in them, to give them small sums in such cases, using tact and discretion about it. I am regularly supplied with funds for this purpose by good women and men in Boston, Salem, Providence, Brooklyn, and New York. I provide myself with a quantity of bright new ten-cent and five-cent bills, and, when I think it incumbent, I give twenty-five or thirty cents, or perhaps fifty cents, and occasionally a still larger sum to some particular case.

As I have started this subject, I take opportunity to ventilate the financial question. My supplies, altogether voluntary, mostly confidential, often seeming quite Providential, were numerous and varied. For instance, there were two distant and wealthy ladies, sisters, who sent regularly, for two years, quite heavy sums, enjoining that their names should be kept secret. The same delicacy was indeed a frequent condition. From several I had *carte blanche*. Many were entire strangers. From these sources, during from two to three years, in the manner described, in the hospitals, I bestowed, as almoner for others, many, many thousands of dollars.

I learn'd one thing conclusively—that beneath all the ostensible greed and heartlessness of our times there is no end to the generous benevolence of men and women in the United States, when once sure of their object. Another thing became clear to me—while *cash* is not amiss to bring up the rear, tact and magnetic sympathy and unction are, and ever will be, sovereign still.

Down at the Front

Falmouth, Va., opposite Fredericksburg, December 21, 1862. Begin my visits among the camp hospitals in the army of the Potomac. Spend a good part of the day in a large brick mansion on the banks of the Rappahannock, used as a hospital since the battle—seems to have receiv'd only the worst cases. Outdoors, at the foot of a tree, within ten yards of the front of the house, I noticed a heap of amputated feet, legs, arms, hands, etc., a full load for a one-horse cart. Several dead bodies lie near, each cover'd with its brown woollen blanket. In the dooryard, toward the river, are fresh graves, mostly of officers, their names on pieces of barrel staves or broken boards, stuck in the dirt. (Most of these bodies were subsequently taken up and transported north to their friends.)

The large mansion is quite crowded upstairs and down, everything impromptu, no system, all bad enough, but I have no doubt the best that can be done; all the wounds pretty bad, some frightful, the men in their old clothes, unclean and bloody. Some of the wounded are rebel soldiers and officers, prisoners. One, a Mississippian, a captain, hit badly in leg, I talk'd with some time; he ask'd me for papers, which I gave him. (I saw him three months afterward in Washington, with his leg amputated, doing well.) I went through the rooms, downstairs and up. Some of the men were dying. I had nothing to give at that visit, but wrote a few letters to home folks, mothers, etc. Also talk'd to three or four, who seem'd most susceptible to it, and needing it.

Last-needed Proof of Democracy

ONE NIGHT in the gloomiest period of the war, in the Patent Office hospital in Washington city, as I stood by the bedside of a Pennsylvania soldier, who lay, conscious of quick approaching death, yet perfectly calm, and with noble, spiritual manner, the veteran surgeon, turning aside, said to me, that though he had witnessed many, many deaths of soldiers, and had been a worker at Bull Run, Antietam, Fredericksburg, etc., he had not seen yet the first case of man or boy that met the approach of dissolution with cowardly qualms or terror. My own observation fully bears out the remark.

What have we here, if not, towering above all talk and argument, the plentifully supplied, last-needed proof of democracy, in its personalities? Curiously enough, too, the proof on this point comes, I should say, every bit as much from the South, as from the North. Although I have spoken only of the latter, yet I deliberately include all. Grand, common stock!

Unnamed Remains the Bravest Soldier

OF SCENES LIKE THESE, I say, who writes—whoe'er can write the story? Of many a score—aye, thousands, North and South, of unwrit heroes, unknown heroisms, incredible, impromptu, first-class desperations—who tells? No history ever—no poem sings, no music sounds, those bravest men of all—those deeds. No formal general's report, nor book in the library, nor column in the paper, embalms the bravest, North or South, East or West. Unnamed, unknown, remain, and still remain, the bravest soldiers. Our manliest—our boys—our hardy darlings; no picture gives them.

Likely, the typic one of them (standing, no doubt, for hundreds, thousands), crawls aside to some bush clump, or ferny tuft, on receiving his death shot—there sheltering a little while, soaking roots, grass and soil, with red blood—the battle advances, retreats, flits from the scene, sweeps by—and there, haply with pain and suffering (yet less, far less than is supposed), the last lethargy winds like a serpent round him—the eyes glaze in death —none recks—perhaps the burial squads, in truce, a week afterward, search not the secluded spot—and there, at last, the Bravest Soldier crumbles in mother earth, unburied and unknown.

Spiritual Characters Among the Soldiers

EVERY NOW AND THEN, in hospital or camp, there are beings I meet—specimens of unworldliness, disinterestedness, and animal purity and heroism—perhaps some unconscious Indianian, or from Ohio or Tennessee—on whose birth the calmness of heaven seems to have descended, and whose gradual growing up, whatever the circumstances of work-life or change, or hardship, or small or no education that attended it, the power of a strange spiritual sweetness, fiber, and inward health, have also attended. Something veil'd and abstracted is often a part of the manners of these beings.

I have met them, I say, not seldom in the army in camp, and in the hospitals. The Western regiments contain many of them. They are often young men, obeying the events and occasions about them, marching, soldiering, fighting, foraging, cooking, working on farms or at some trade before the war—unaware of their own nature (as to that, who is aware of his own nature?) their companions only understanding that they are different from the rest, more silent, "something odd about them," and apt to go off and meditate and muse in solitude.

Fifty Hours Left Wounded on the Field

HERE IS A CASE of a soldier I found among the crowded cots in the Patent Office. He likes to have someone to talk to, and we will listen to him. He got badly hit in his leg and side at Fredericksburg that eventful Saturday, 13th of December. He lay the succeeding two days and nights helpless on the field, between the city and those grim terraces of batteries; his company and regiment had been compell'd to leave him to his fate. To make matters worse, it happen'd he lay with his head slightly down hill, and could not help himself. At the end of some fifty hours he was brought off, with other wounded, under a flag of truce.

I ask him how the rebels treated him as he lay during those two days and nights within reach of them—whether they came to him—whether they abused him? He answers that several of the rebels, soldiers and others, came to him at one time and another. A couple of them, who were together, spoke roughly and sarcastically, but nothing worse.

One middle-aged man, however, who seem'd to be moving around the field, among the dead and wounded, for benevolent purposes, came to him in a way he will never forget; treated our soldier kindly, bound up his wounds, cheer'd him, gave him a couple of biscuits and a drink of whisky and water; asked him if he could eat some beef. This good secesh, however, did not change our soldier's position, for it might have caused the blood to burst from the wounds, clotted and stagnated.

Our soldier is from Pennsylvania; has had a pretty severe time; the wounds proved to be bad ones. But he retains a good heart, and is at present on the gain. (It is not uncommon for the men to remain on the field this way, one, two, or even four or five days.)

Boys in the Army

As I walk'd home about sunset, I saw in Fourteenth Street a very young soldier, thinly clad, standing near the house I was about to enter. I stopped a moment in front of the door and call'd him to me. I knew that an old Tennessee regiment, and also an Indiana regiment, were temporarily stopping in new barracks, near Fourteenth Street. This boy I found belonged to the Tennessee regiment. But I could hardly believe he carried a musket.

He was but fifteen years old, yet had been twelve months a soldier, and had borne his part in several battles, even historic ones. I ask'd him if he did not suffer from the cold, and if he had no overcoat. No, he did not suffer from cold, and had no overcoat, but could draw one whenever he wish'd. His father was dead, and his mother living in some part of East Tennessee; all the men were from that part of the country. The next forenoon I saw the Tennessee and Indiana regiments marching down the avenue. My boy was with the former, stepping along with the rest.

There were many other boys no older. I stood and watch'd them as they tramp'd along with slow, strong, heavy, regular steps. There did not appear to be a man over thirty years of age, and a large proportion were from fifteen to perhaps twenty-two or twenty-three. They had all the look of veterans, worn, stain'd, impassive, and a certain unbent, lounging gait, carrying in addition to their regular arms and knapsacks, frequently a frying pan, broom, etc. They were all of pleasant physiognomy; no refinement, nor blanch'd with intellect, but as my eye pick'd them, moving along, rank by rank, there did not seem to be a single repulsive, brutal or markedly stupid face among them.

Releas'd Prisoners From the South

THE RELEAS'D PRISONERS OF WAR are now coming up from the Southern prisons. I have seen a number of them. The sight is worse than any sight of battlefields, or any collection of wounded, even the bloodiest. There was (as a sample), one large boatload, of several hundreds, brought about the 25th, to Annapolis; and out of the whole number only three individuals were able to walk from the boat. The rest were carried ashore and laid down in one place or another.

Can those be *men*—those little livid brown, ash-streak'd, monkey-looking dwarfs?—are they really not mummied, dwindled corpses? They lay there, most of them, quite still, but with a horrible look in their eyes and skinny lips (often with not enough flesh on the lips to cover their teeth).

Probably no more appalling sight was ever seen on this earth. (There are deeds, crimes, that may be forgiven; but this is not among them. It steeps its perpetrators in blackest, escapeless, endless damnation. Over fifty thousand have been compell'd to die the death of starvation—reader, did you ever try to realize what *starvation* actually is?—in those prisons—and in a land of plenty.) An indescribable meanness, tyranny, aggravating course of insults, almost incredible—was evidently the rule of treatment through all the Southern military prisons. The dead there are not to be pitied as much as some of the living that come from there—if they can be call'd living—many of them are mentally imbecile, and will never recuperate.

Three Years Summ'd Up

DURING THOSE THREE YEARS in hospital, camp, or field, I made over six hundred visits or tours, and went, as I estimate, counting all, among from eighty thousand to a hundred thousand of the wounded and sick, as sustainer of spirit and body in some degree, in time of need. These visits varied from an hour or two, to all day or night; for with dear or critical cases I generally watch'd all night. Sometimes I took up my quarters in the hospital, and slept or watch'd there several nights in succession.

Those three years I consider the greatest privilege and satisfaction (with all their feverish excitements and physical deprivations and lamentable sights) and, of course, the most profound lesson of my life. I can say that in my ministerings I comprehended all, whoever came in my way, Northern or Southern, and slighted none. It arous'd and brought out and decided undreamt-

of depths of emotion. It has given me my most fervent views of the true *ensemble* and extent of the States. While I was with wounded and sick in thousands of cases from the New England States, and from New York, New Jersey, and Pennsylvania, and from Michigan, Wisconsin, Ohio, Indiana, Illinois, and all the Western States, I was with more or less from all the States, North and South, without exception.

I was with many from the border States, especially from Maryland and Virginia, and found, during those lurid years 1862-63, far more Union Southerners, especially Tennesseans, than is supposed. I was with many rebel officers and men among our wounded, and gave them always what I had, and tried to cheer them the same as any. I was among the army teamsters considerably, and, indeed, always found myself drawn to them. Among the black soldiers, wounded or sick, and in the contraband camps, I also took my way whenever in their neighborhood, and did what I could for them.

The Million Dead, Too, Summ'd Up

THE DEAD IN THIS WAR—there they lie, strewing the fields and woods and valleys and battlefields of the south—Virginia, the Peninsula—Malvern Hill and Fair Oaks—the banks of the Chickahominy—the terraces of Fredericksburg—Antietam bridge—the grisly ravines of Manassas—the bloody promenade of the Wilderness—the varieties of the *strayed* dead (the estimate of the War department is 25,000 national soldiers kill'd in battle and never buried at all, 5,000 drown'd—15,000 inhumed by strangers, or on the march in haste, in hitherto unfound localities—2,000 graves cover'd by sand and mud by Mississippi freshets, 3,000 carried away by caving-in of banks, etc.)—Gettysburg, the West, Southwest, Vicksburg—Chattanooga—the trenches of Petersburg—the numberless battles, camps, hospitals everywhere—the crop reap'd by the mighty reapers, typhoid, dysentery, inflammations and blackest and loathsomest of all, the dead and living, burial pits, the prison pens of Andersonville, Salisbury, Belle Isle, etc. (not Dante's pictured hell and all its woes, its degradations, filthy torments, excell'd those prisons)—the dead, the dead, the dead—*our* dead—or South or North, ours all (all, all, all, finally dear to me)—or East or West—Atlantic coast or Mississippi valley—somewhere they crawl'd to die, alone, in bushes, low gullies, or on the sides of hills—(there, in secluded spots, their skeletons, bleach'd bones, tufts of hair, buttons, fragments of clothing, are occasionally found yet)—our young men once so handsome and so joyous taken from us—the son from the mother, the husband from the wife, the dear friend from the dear friend—the clusters of camp graves, in Georgia, the Carolinas, and in Tennessee—the single graves left in the woods or by the roadside (hundreds, thousands, obliterated)—the corpses floated down the rivers, and caught and lodged (dozens, scores, floated down the upper Potomac, after the cavalry engagements, the pursuit of Lee, following Gettysburg)—some lie at the bottom of the sea—the general million, and the special cemeteries in almost all the States—the infinite dead—(the land entire saturated, perfumed with their impalpable ashes' exhalation in Nature's chemistry distill'd, and shall be so forever, in every future grain of wheat and ear of corn, and every flower that grows, and every breath we draw)—not only Northern leavening Southern soil—thousands, aye tens of thousands, of Southerners, crumble today in Northern earth.

And everywhere among these countless graves—everywhere in the many soldier cemeteries of the nation, (there are now, I believe, over seventy of them)—as at the time in the vast trenches, the depositories of slain, Northern and Southern, after the great battles—not only where the scathing trail passed those years, but radiating since in all the peaceful quarters of the land—we see, and ages yet may see, on monuments and gravestones, singly or in masses to thousands or tens of thousands, the significant word Unknown.

The Real War Will Never Get in the Books

FUTURE YEARS will never know the seething hell and the black infernal background of countless minor scenes and interiors, (not the official surface-courteousness of the Generals, not the few great battles) of the Secession War; and it is best they should not —the real war will never get in the books.

Such was the war. It was not a quadrille in a ballroom. Its interior history will not only never be written—its practicality, minutiae of deeds and passions will never be even suggested. The actual soldier of 1862-65, North and South, with all his ways, his incredible dauntlessness, habits, practices, tastes, language, his fierce friendship, his appetite, rankness, his superb strength and animality, lawless gait, and a hundred unnamed lights and shades of camp, I say, will never be written—perhaps must not and should not be.

The preceding notes may furnish a few stray glimpses into that life, and into those lurid interiors, never to be fully convey'd to the future. The hospital part of the drama from '61 to '65 deserves indeed to be recorded. Of that many-threaded drama, with its sudden and strange surprises, its confounding of prophecies, its moments of despair, the dread of foreign interference, the interminable campaigns, the bloody battles, the mighty and cumbrous and green armies, the drafts and bounties—the immense money expenditure, like a heavy-pouring constant rain—with, over the whole land, the last three years of the struggle an unending, universal mourning-wail of women, parents, orphans—the marrow of the tragedy concentrated in those army hospitals—(it seem'd sometimes as if the whole interest of the land, North and South, was one vast central hospital, and all the rest of the affair but flanges—those forming the untold and unwritten history of the war—infinitely greater (like life's) than the few scraps and distortions that are ever told or written.

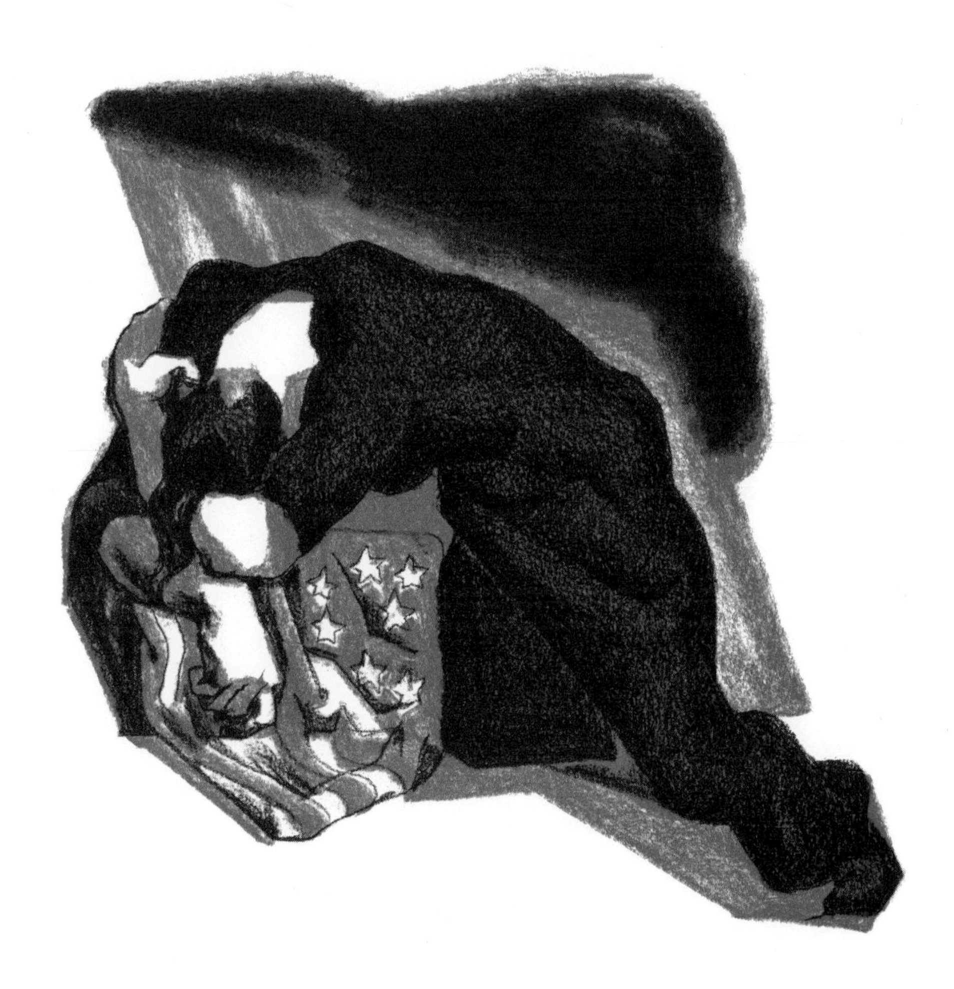

Abraham Lincoln

The First Time I Ever Saw Abraham Lincoln

I SHALL NOT EASILY FORGET the first time I ever saw Abraham Lincoln. It must have been about the 18th or 19th of February, 1861. It was rather a pleasant afternoon, in New York City, as he arrived there from the West, to remain a few hours, and then pass on to Washington, to prepare for his inauguration.

I saw him in Broadway, near the site of the present Post Office. He came down, I think from Canal Street, to stop at the Astor House. The broad spaces, sidewalks, and streets in the neighborhood, and for some distance, were crowded with solid masses of people, many thousands. The omnibuses and other vehicles had all been turn'd off, leaving an unusual hush in that busy part of the city. Presently two or three shabby hack barouches made their way with some difficulty through the crowd, and drew up at the Astor House entrance. A tall figure step'd out of the center of these barouches, paus'd leisurely on the sidewalk, look'd up at the granite walls and looming architecture of the grand old hotel—then, after a relieving stretch of arms and legs, turn'd round for over a minute to slowly and good-humoredly scan the appearance of the vast and silent crowds.

There were no speeches—no compliments—no welcome—as far as I could hear, not a word said. Still much anxiety was conceal'd in that quiet. Cautious persons had fear'd some mark'd insult or indignity to the President-elect—for he possess'd no personal popularity at all in New York City, and very little political. But it was evidently tacitly agreed that if the few political supporters of Mr. Lincoln present would entirely abstain from any demonstration on their side, the immense majority, who were anything but supporters, would abstain on their side also. The result was a sulky, unbroken silence, such as certainly never before characterized so great a New York crowd.

Almost in the same neighborhood I distinctly remember'd seeing Lafayette on his visit to America in 1825. I had also personally seen and heard, various years afterward, how Andrew Jackson, Clay, Webster, Hungarian Kossuth, Filibuster Walker, the Prince of Wales on his visit, and other celebres, native and foreign, had been welcom'd there—all that indescribable human roar and magnetism, unlike any other sound in the universe—the glad exulting thunder-shouts of countless unloos'd throats of men! But on this occasion, not a voice—not a sound.

From the top of an omnibus (driven up one side, close by, and block'd by the curbstone and the crowds), I had, I say, a capital view of it all, and especially of Mr. Lincoln, his look and gait—his perfect composure and coolness—his unusual and uncouth height, his dress of complete black, stovepipe hat push'd back on the head, dark-brown complexion, seam'd and wrinkled yet canny-looking face, black, bushy head of hair, disproportionately long neck, and his hands held behind as he stood observing the people. He look'd with curiosity upon that immense sea of faces, and the sea of faces return'd the look with similar curiosity. In both there was a dash of comedy, almost farce, such as Shakespere puts in his blackest tragedies. The crowd that hemm'd around consisted I should think of thirty to forty thousand men, not a single one his personal friend—while I have no doubt (so frenzied were the ferments of the time), many an assassin's knife and pistol lurk'd in hip or breast-pocket there, ready, soon as break and riot came.

But no break or riot came. The tall figure gave another relieving stretch or two of arms and legs; then with moderate pace, and accompanied by a few unknown looking persons, ascended the portico-steps of the Astor House, disappear'd through its broad entrance—and the dumb-show ended.

I See the President Almost Every Day

August 12. [1863] I see the President almost every day, as I happen to live where he passes to or from his lodgings out of town. He never sleeps at the White House during the hot season, but has quarters at a healthy location some three miles north of the city, the Soldiers' Home, a United States military establishment. I saw him this morning about 8:30 coming in to business, riding on Vermont Avenue, near L Street. He always has a company of twenty-five or thirty cavalry, with sabers drawn and held upright over their shoulders. They say this guard was against his personal wish, but he let his counselors have their way.

The party makes no great show in uniform or horses. Mr. Lincoln on the saddle generally rides a good-sized, easygoing gray horse, is dress'd in plain black, somewhat rusty and dusty, wears a black stiff hat, and looks about as ordinary in attire, etc., as the commonest man. A lieutenant, with yellow straps, rides at his left, and following behind, two by two, come the cavalry men, in their yellow-striped jackets. They are generally going at a slow trot, as that is the pace set them by the one they wait upon. The sabers and accouterments clank, and the entirely unornamental *cortège* as it trots toward Lafayette Square arouses no sensation, only some curious stranger stops and gazes. I see very plainly Abraham Lincoln's dark brown face, with the deep-cut lines, the eyes, always to me with a deep latent sadness in the expression. We have got so that we exchange bows, and very cordial ones.

Sometimes the President goes and comes in an open barouche. The cavalry always accompany him, with drawn sabers. Often I

notice as he goes out evenings—and sometimes in the mornings, when he returns early—he turns off and halts at the large and handsome residence of the Secretary of War, on K Street, and holds conference there. If in his barouche, I can see from my window he does not alight, but sits in his vehicle, and Mr. Stanton comes out to attend him. Sometimes one of his sons, a boy of ten or twelve, accompanies him, riding at his right on a pony.

Earlier in the summer I occasionally saw the President and his wife, toward the latter part of the afternoon, out in a barouche, on a pleasure ride through the city. Mrs. Lincoln was dress'd in complete black, with a long crape veil. The equipage is of the plainest kind, only two horses, and they nothing extra. They pass'd me once very close, and I saw the President in the face fully, as they were moving slowly, and his look, though abstracted, happen'd to be directed steadily in my eye. He bow'd and smiled, but far beneath his smile I noticed well the expression I have alluded to. None of the artists or pictures has caught the deep, though subtle and indirect expression of this man's face. There is something else there. One of the great portrait painters of two or three centuries ago is needed.

Such Was Lincoln's Face

PROBABLY THE READER has seen physiognomies (often old farmers, sea captains, and such) that, behind their homeliness, or even ugliness, held superior points so subtle, yet so palpable, making the real life of their faces almost as impossible to depict as a wild perfume or fruit taste, or a passionate tone of the living voice—and such was Lincoln's face, the peculiar color, the lines of it, the eyes, mouth, expression. Of technical beauty it had nothing—but to the eye of a great artist it furnished a rare study, a feast and fascination. The current portraits are all failures—most of them caricatures.

The Inauguration and the Inauguration Ball

March 4 [1865]. The President very quietly rode down to the Capitol in his own carriage, by himself, on a sharp trot, about noon, either because he wish'd to be on hand to sign bills, or to get rid of marching in line with the absurd procession, the muslin temple of liberty, and pasteboard monitor. I saw him on his return, at three o'clock, after the performance was over.

He was in his plain two-horse barouche, and look'd very much worn and tired; the lines, indeed, of vast responsibilities, intricate questions, and demands of life and death, cut deeper than ever upon his dark brown face; yet all the old goodness, tenderness, sadness, and canny shrewdness, underneath the furrows. (I never see that man without feeling that he is one to become personally attach'd to, for his combination of purest, heartiest tenderness, and native western form of manliness.) By his side sat his little boy, of ten years. There were no soldiers, only a lot of civilians on horseback, with huge yellow scarfs over their shoulders, riding around the carriage. (At the inauguration four years ago, he rode down and back again surrounded by a dense mass of arm'd cavalrymen eight deep, with drawn sabers; and there were sharpshooters station'd at every corner on the route.)

I ought to make mention of the closing levée of Saturday night last. Never before was such a compact jam in front of the White House—all the grounds fill'd, and away out to the spacious sidewalks. I was there, as I took a notion to go—was in the rush inside with the crowd—surged along the passageways, the blue and other rooms, and through the great east room. Crowds of country people, some very funny. Fine music from the Marine band, off in a side place. I saw Mr. Lincoln, drest all in black, with white kid gloves and a claw-hammer coat, receiving, as in duty bound, shaking hands, looking very disconsolate, and as if he would give anything to be somewhere else.

March 6. I have been up to look at the dance and supper room, for the inauguration ball at the Patent Office; and I could not help thinking, what a different scene they presented to my view a while since, fill'd with a crowded mass of the worst wounded of the war, brought in from second Bull Run, Antietam, and Fredericksburg. Tonight, beautiful women, perfumes, the violins' sweetness, the polka and the waltz; then the amputation, the blue face, the groan, the glassy eye of the dying, the clotted rag, the odor of wounds and blood, and many a mother's son amid strangers, passing away untended there (for the crowd of the badly hurt was great, and much for nurse to do, and much for surgeon).

The Assassination

The popular afternoon paper of Washington, the little "Evening Star," had spatter'd all over its third page, divided among the advertisements in a sensational manner, in a hundred different places, *The President and his Lady will be at the Theater this evening. . . .* (Lincoln was fond of the theater. I have myself seen him there several times. I remember thinking how funny it was that he, in some respects the leading actor in the stormiest drama known to real history's stage through centuries, should sit there and be so completely interested and absorb'd in those human jack-straws, moving about with their silly little gestures, foreign spirit, and flatulent text.)

On this occasion the theater was crowded, many ladies in rich and gay costumes, officers in their uniforms, many well-known citizens, young folks, the usual clusters of gas lights, the usual magnetism of so many people, cheerful, with perfumes, music of violins and flutes—(and over all, and saturating all, that vast, vague wonder, *Victory,* the nation's victory, the triumph of the Union, filling the air, the thought, the sense, with exhilaration more than all music and perfumes.)

The President came betimes, and, with his wife, witness'd the play from the large stage boxes of the second tier, two thrown into one, and profusely draped with the national flag. The acts and scenes of the piece—one of those singularly written compositions which have at least the merit of giving entire relief to an audience engaged in mental action or business excitements and cares during the day, as it makes not the slightest call on either the moral, emotional, esthetic, or spiritual nature—a piece ("Our American Cousin") in which, among other characters, so call'd, a Yankee, certainly such a one as was never seen, or the least like it ever seen, in North America, is introduced in England, with a varied folderol of talk, plot, scenery, and such phantasmagoria as goes to make up a modern popular drama—had progress'd through perhaps a couple of its acts, when in the midst of this comedy, or non-such, or whatever it is to be call'd, and to offset it, or finish it out, as if in Nature's and the great Muse's mockery of those poor mimes, came interpolated that scene, not really or exactly to be described at all (for on the many hundreds who were there it seems to this hour to have left a passing blur, a dream, a blotch)—and yet partially to be described as I now proceed to give it.

There is a scene in the play representing a modern parlor, in which two unprecedented English ladies are inform'd by the impossible Yankee that he is not a man of fortune, and therefore undesirable for marriage-catching purposes; after which, the comments being finish'd, the dramatic trio make exit, leaving the stage clear for a moment. At this period came the murder of Abraham Lincoln. Great as all its manifold train, circling round it, and stretching into the future for many a century, in the politics, history, art, etc., of the New World, in point of fact the main thing, the actual murder, transpired with the quiet and simplicity of any commonest occurrence—the bursting of a bud or pod in the growth of vegetation, for instance.

Through the general hum following the stage pause, with the change of positions, came the muffled sound of a pistol shot, which not one-hundredth part of the audience heard at the time —and yet a moment's hush—somehow, surely, a vague startled thrill—and then, through the ornamented, draperied, starr'd and striped space-way of the President's box, a sudden figure, a man, raises himself with hands and feet, stands a moment on the railing, leaps below to the stage (a distance of perhaps fourteen or fifteen feet), falls out of position, catching his boot heel in the copious drapery (the American flag), falls on one knee, quickly recovers himself, rises as if nothing had happen'd (he really sprains his ankle, but unfelt then)—and so the figure, Booth, the murderer, dress'd in plain black broadcloth, bare-headed, with full, glossy, raven hair, and his eyes like some mad animal's flashing with light and resolution, yet with a certain strange calmness, holds aloft in one hand a large knife—walks along not much back from the footlights—turns fully toward the audience his face of statuesque beauty, lit by those basilisk eyes, flashing with desperation, perhaps insanity—launches out in a firm and steady voice the words *Sic semper tyrannis*—and then walks with neither slow nor very rapid pace diagonally across to the back of the stage, and disappears. (Had not all this terrible scene—making the mimic ones preposterous—had it not all been rehears'd, in blank, by Booth, beforehand?)

A moment's hush—a scream—the cry of *murder*—Mrs. Lincoln leaning out of the box, with ashy cheeks and lips, with involuntary cry, pointing to the retreating figure, *He has kill'd the President*. And still a moment's strange, incredulous suspense—and then the deluge!—then that mixture of horror, noises, uncertainty —(the sound, somewhere back, of a horse's hoofs clattering with speed)—the people burst through chairs and railings, and break them up—there is inextricable confusion and terror—women faint—quite feeble persons fall, and are trampled on—many cries of agony are heard—the broad stage suddenly fills to suffocation with a dense and motley crowd, like some horrible carnival—the audience rush generally upon it, at least the strong men do—the actors and actresses are all there in their play costumes and painted faces, with mortal fright showing through the rouge—the screams and calls, confused talk—redoubled, trebled—two or three manage to pass up water from the stage to the President's box—others try to clamber up—etc., etc.

In the midst of all this, the soldiers of the President's guard, with others, suddenly drawn to the scene, burst in—(some two hundred altogether)—they storm the house, through all the tiers, especially the upper ones, inflamed with fury, literally charging the audience with fix'd bayonets, muskets and pistols, shouting *Clear out! clear out! you sons of* ——. . . . . Such the wild scene, or a suggestion of it rather, inside the play-house that night.

Outside, too, in the atmosphere of shock and craze, crowds of people, fill'd with frenzy, ready to seize any outlet for it, come near committing murder several times on innocent individuals. One such case was especially exciting. The infuriated crowd, through some chance, got started against one man, either for words he utter'd, or perhaps without any cause at all, and were proceeding at once to actually hang him on a neighboring lamp-post, when he was rescued by a few heroic policemen, who placed him in their midst, and fought their way slowly and amid great peril toward the station house. It was a fitting episode of the whole affair. The crowd rushing and eddying to and fro—the night, the yells, the pale faces, many frighten'd people trying in vain to extricate themselves—the attack'd man, not yet freed from the jaws of death, looking like a corpse—the silent, resolute,

half-dozen policemen, with no weapons but their little clubs, yet stern and steady through all those eddying swarms—made a fitting side-scene to the grand tragedy of the murder. They gain'd the station house with the protected man, whom they placed in security for the night, and discharged him in the morning.

And in the midst of that pandemonium, infuriated soldiers, the audience and the crowd, the stage, and all its actors and actresses, its paint pots, spangles, and gas lights—the life blood from those veins, the best and sweetest of the land, drips slowly down, and death's ooze already begins its little bubbles on the lips.

Thus the visible incidents and surroundings of Abraham Lincoln's murder, as they really occur'd.

APRIL 16, 1865. I FIND IN MY NOTES OF THE TIME, THIS PASSAGE ON THE DEATH OF ABRAHAM LINCOLN: HE LEAVES FOR AMERICA'S HISTORY AND BIOGRAPHY, SO FAR, NOT ONLY ITS MOST DRAMATIC REMINISCENCE—HE LEAVES, IN MY OPINION, THE GREATEST, BEST, MOST CHARACTERISTIC, ARTISTIC, MORAL PERSONALITY. NOT BUT THAT HE HAD FAULTS, AND SHOW'D THEM IN THE PRESIDENCY; BUT HONESTY, GOODNESS, SHREWDNESS, CONSCIENCE, AND (A NEW VIRTUE, UNKNOWN TO OTHER LANDS, AND HARDLY YET REALLY KNOWN HERE, BUT THE FOUNDATION AND TIE OF ALL, AS THE FUTURE WILL GRANDLY DEVELOP), UNIONISM, IN ITS TRUEST AND AMPLEST SENSE, FORM'D THE HARD-PAN OF HIS CHARACTER. THESE HE SEAL'D WITH HIS LIFE.

THE TRAGIC SPLENDOR OF HIS DEATH, PURGING, ILLUMINATING ALL, THROWS ROUND HIS FORM, HIS HEAD, AN AUREOLE THAT WILL REMAIN AND WILL GROW BRIGHTER THROUGH TIME, WHILE HISTORY LIVES, AND LOVE OF COUNTRY LASTS. BY MANY HAS THIS UNION BEEN HELP'D; BUT IF ONE NAME, ONE MAN, MUST BE PICK'D OUT, HE, MOST OF ALL, IS THE CONSERVATOR OF IT, TO THE FUTURE. HE WAS ASSASSINATED—BUT THE UNION IS NOT ASSASSINATED—*ÇA IRA!* ONE FALLS, AND ANOTHER FALLS. THE SOLDIER DROPS, SINKS LIKE A WAVE, BUT THE RANKS OF THE OCEAN ETERNALLY PRESS ON. DEATH DOES ITS WORK, OBLITERATES A HUNDRED, A THOUSAND—PRESIDENT, GENERAL, CAPTAIN, PRIVATE—